The UPSIDE DOWN FROWN

SHAPE POETRY

collected by Andrew Fusek Peters

The ✦ Hall

Hampstead

Middle School

WAYLAND

CONTENTS

Wayland Paperback Poetry

The Upside Down Frown
Collected by Andrew Fusek Peters

The Worst Class In School
Collected by Brian Moses

THE UPSIDE DOWN FROWN

First published in 1999 by
Wayland (Publishers) Ltd
61 Western Rd, Hove
East Sussex BN3 1JD, England
www.wayland.co.uk

This collection © Wayland Publishers Ltd 1999

Commissioning Editor: Paul Mason (paulm@wayland.co.uk)
Production Controller: Carol Titchener
Designer/typesetter: Danny McBride

The compiler and publishers would like to thank the authors for allowing their poems to appear in this collection. While every attempt has been made to gain permissions, in some cases this has not been possible and we apologise for any omissions.

British Library Cataloguing in Publication Data is available for this title.

ISBN 0 7502 2541 6

Printed in Hong Kong by Wing King Tong.

Mary Booster had a hooter
the shape of a giant-sized
pea shooter.
So every time she tried to sneeze,
out shot a pile of
mushy peas.

MARY'S HOOTER

Andrew Collett

4

Colin West

Me
and
Amanda
meander,
like
rivers
that
run
to
the
sea.
We
wander
at
random
we're
always
in
tandem:
meandering
Mandy
and
me.

SISTERS

Gina Douthwaite

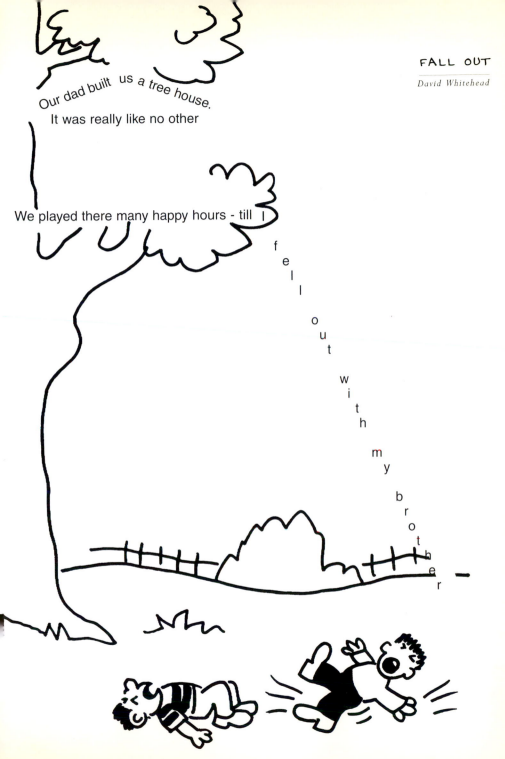

Our dad built us a tree house.
It was really like no other

We played there many happy hours - till I
f
e
l
l
o
u
t
w
i
t
h
m
y
b
r
o
t
h
e
r

ROLLING DOWN A HILL

Colin West

I'm rolling
rolling
rolling
down

I'm rolling
down a
hill.

I'm rolling
rolling
rolling
down

I'm rolling
down it
still.

I'm rolling
rolling
down

I'm rolling
down a
hill.

I'm rolling
rolling
down

But now
I'm feeling
ill.

Ian Souter

Zoom down the banisters heading south, but waiting at the bottom is Mum's angry M O UTH

Roger McGough

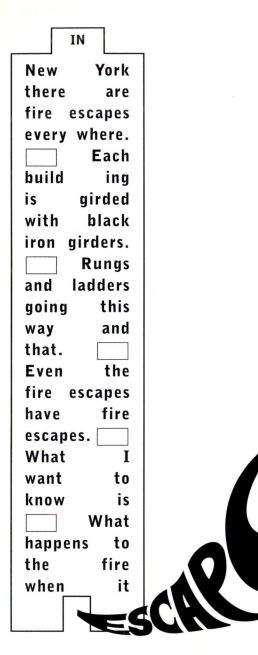

IN

New York
there are
fire escapes
every where.
☐ Each
build ing
is girded
with black
iron girders.
☐ Rungs
and ladders
going this
way and
that. ☐
Even the
fire escapes
have fire
escapes. ☐
What I
want to
know is
☐ What
happens to
the fire
when it

ESCAPES

Matt Simpson

DEAD BIRD

HUMPTY

Jane Yolen

Humpty Dumpty was not eggs-actly your average kind of a guy.

A WEE BIT CRACKED, HE SAT
ON A WALL AND WATCHED
THE WORLD GO BY

A poet? A dreamer?

A teller of tales? He was.

And so am I.

I. Souter

When you are sad and wearing a frown,
Then try turning this poem upside down

BULLY
Andrew Collett

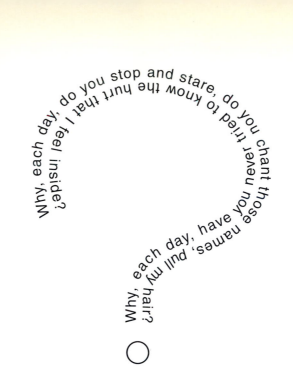

Why, each day, do you stop and stare, do you chant those names, pull my hair? Why, each day, have you never tried to know the hurt that I feel inside? Why, each day, do you stop and stare, do you chant those names, pull my hair?

HIM
Clare Bevan

HE IS SO BIG

I am so small

at playtime I wish

I was not there

at all

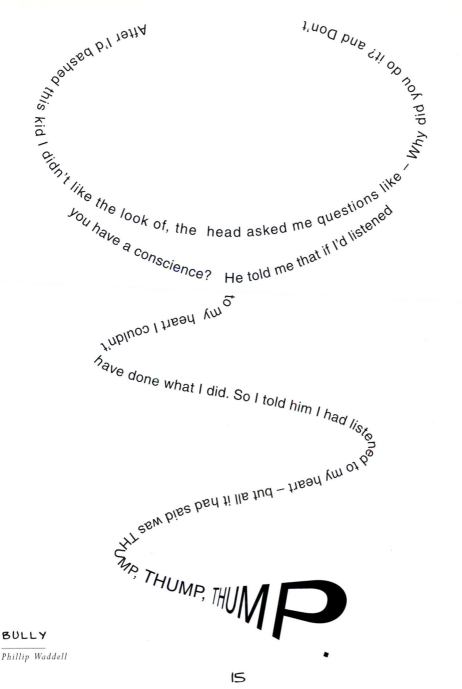

After I'd bashed this kid I didn't like the look of, the head asked me questions like — Why did you do it? and Don't you have a conscience? He told me that if I'd listened to my heart I couldn't have done what I did. So I told him I had listened to my heart — but all it had said was THUMP, THUMP, THUMP.

BULLY

Phillip Waddell

15

SPECTACLES
Andrew Collett

Look

A
poem
is just
like a tear:
a drop
of emotion
- a time explosion
- a silent
commotion
- an act of
devotion
-

TEAR
James Carter

16

Roger Stevens

treetreetreetree
treetreetreetreetreetreetreetreetreetree
treetreetreetreetreetreetreetreetreetreetreetree
treetreetreetreetreetreetreetreetreetreetreetree
treetreetreetree**you**tree**can**tree**search**tree**all**tree**day**tre
treetreetreetreetreetreetreetreetreetreetreetreetreetreetree
eetreetree**but**tree**you'll**tree**never**tree**see**treetreetreetreee
treetreetreetreetreetreetreetreetreetreetreetreetreetreetree
etreetreetree**the**tree**chameleon**tree**hiding**treetreetreetree
treetreetreetreetreetreetreetreetreetreetreetreetreetreetree
etreetree**in**tree**the**treetreetreetreetreetreetreetreetreetre
treetreetreetreetreetreetreetreetreetreetreetreetreetree
eetreetreetreetreetreetreetreetreetreetreetreetreetr
eetreetreetreetreetreetreetreetreetreetreetreetreet
eetreetreetreetreetreetreetreetreetreetreetreetree
etreetreetreetreetreetreetreetreetreetreet
treetreetreetree
treetreet
etreetree
treetree
eetreetr
treetree
etreetre
treetree
reetreetre
etreetreetree
eetreetreetreetre

THE WORM THAT TURNED

Celia Warren

O
here is
the
worm
that
turned
but
not
the other cheek;
this
worm
wrapped
himself
around
the
early bird's
fat
beak.

Dressed in a coat of mud
soil with splattered and
the farm tractor and
throat bad a with horn factory a like
coughs and rasps

Huge tyres heave
churning the through plough the
field soggy the dark earth into
waves frozen like shapes
Seagulls swoop and glide behind
free flowing ribbons wild like
in some great wind.

Up and down
- long day all valley the up and down
the tractor never tires.
pierce lights its evening By
the gathering dusk
growl its and

fields the over echo.
like a tumbling the Slowly, warm dark
night star-filled the silent in a warm that
covers plough the countryside own its brings
rolls the over own

YS OWL

Dave Calder

Waking up in our family tent
we wonder
Sleeping-bag nights are so befuddling,
creeping, crawling caterpillars cuddling!
where the night-time went.

CAMPING CAPERS

John Rice

20

ICICLE RIDE

Nick Toczek

**Oh, how cold it feels
on 5 winter wheels!**

I hum in the summer kitchen, a white box of winter. I make ice while the sun shines. My light flicks on and off at your **whim.** In me you hide fruit of summer, safe from the brown menace of heat which thieves its bloom. Water in me is like the water from mountain pools cooled in my frosty embrace. I bring relief from the midday blistering sun when you clink my gift of ice cubes in squash. Cool   chill.

DAWN POEM

Tony Mitton

UP COMES THE SUN WITH A BIG, RED YAWN

BEHIND A MOUNTAIN, BRINGING THE DAWN,

24

onion moon
in a abowl of
sliver of night
garnish of
light

unravelling day
layers of dark
peels night away
Onion sun

A THOUGHTFUL RIDDLE

Albanian Riddle - translated by Elona Velca and Andrew Fusek Peters

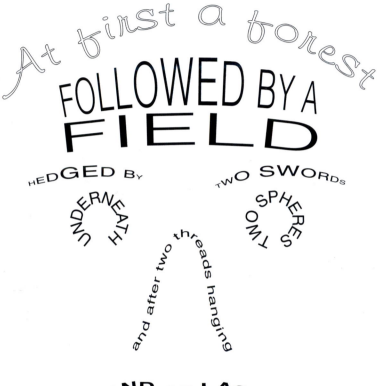

At first a forest
FOLLOWED BY A FIELD
HEDGED BY   TWO SWORDs
UNDERNEATH   TWO SPHERES
and after two threads hanging
AND AT LAST
THE NIGHTINGALE SINGING

All flamingos keep a feather duster underneath their sink so, before they go to bed each night, they can tickle each other pink.

THE LIGHTHOUSE

Gerard Benson

THE LIGHTHOUSE

This is the light
that shines so bright
to warn the shipping
through the night.

This is the beam which sends a stream
of precious light, of golden light
to guide the sailors through the night.

This is the tower
of brick and stone
that stands so tall
and all alone.
It's painted white
and holds the light
that sends a beam
into the night
to warn the sailors
out at sea
of dangerous rocks
that out of sight
could wreck the shipping
in the night.

This is the island rocky and small
that holds the light that stands so tall
to send the beams of precious light
that guide the sailors in the night.

This is the sea
that laps around
and sometimes has a gentle face
and sometimes lashes at the base,
at other times it roars all night
and splashes to an awful height
against the lonely island's light.

28

SEAGULL

Andrew Fusek Peters

SEAGULL SOARS IN FLIGHT FANTASTIC
HIS DOUBLE ROLLS ARE QUITE GYMNASTIC
BUT HOW HE SQUAWKS
A RAUCOUS RACKET
AS ON MY HEAD HE DROPS A PACKET!

Dave Calder

cCCCCCc cCCCCCc
C

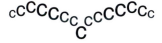

cCCCCCc cCCCCCc
C

winds wail while
wandering wide wallowing
watery wastes,   whisk worried
wrinkles   wound with whipping
wings   which whittle wedges,
whirl, whorl, wrestle
wantonly; which worst
will wake wild weltering
wrath wearing wrenched wrack,
whose whomping writhing wallop
whacks whales, whams wee walruses,
wrecks warships with wuthering weight,
whops worn wharves whose whole works wobble;
wave walls wheeling, whooshing, whanging, whelming,
wrap weeping white webs which wither when woven, wash weary away

wAVE

Dave Calder

Mike Johnson

slimy rainbOws
drift In and out as
tidaL forces tug
seabirdS struggle to get
cLean but only swallow
more slow poIson which
is the priCe of
manKind's so-called progress

SALVAGED

Phillip Waddell

                    This
                     poem
                      is orderly,
                       tidy, organised.
                    There's a place
                   for every letter and
                 every letter's in its place.
                There's a place for every word and every
            word's in its place. There's a place for every sentence
           and every sentence is in its place. It wasn't launched
            like this, at first it was all flotsam in my head
             but now I've salvaged it and it is shipshape.

Tony Mitton

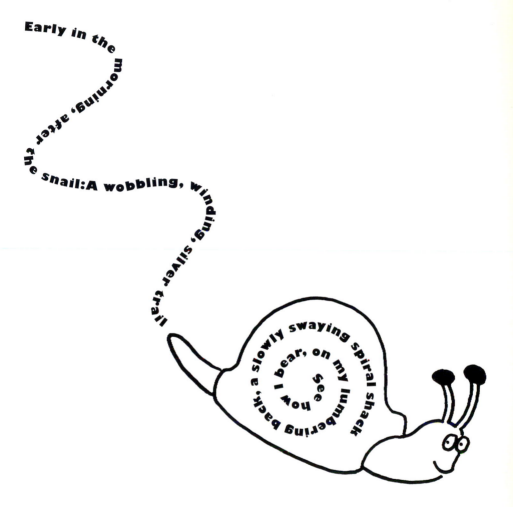

Early in the morning, after the snail: A wobbling, winding, silver trail a slowly swaying spiral shack I bear, on my lumbering back, now I see

GIRAFFE

Dave Calder

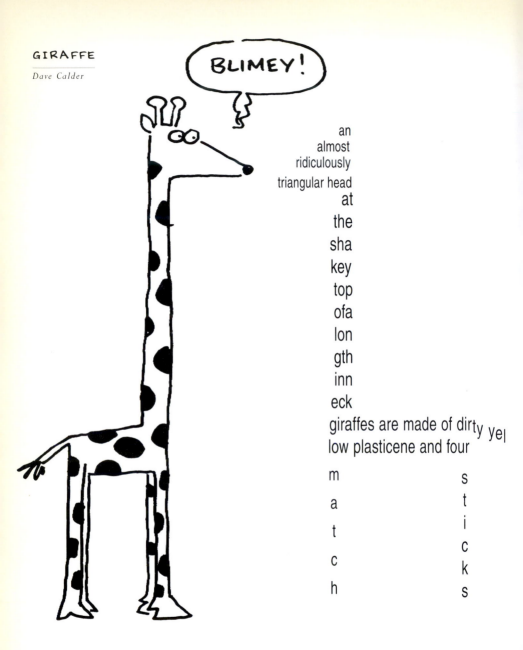

an
almost
ridiculously
triangular head
at
the
sha
key
top
ofa
lon
gth
inn
eck
giraffes are made of dirty yel
low plasticene and four

m   s
a   t
t   i
      c
c   k
h   s

TALL STORY

Mike Johnson

graph

my

on

it

fit

not

could

but

giraffe,

Sir's

measure

to

went

I went to measure Sir's giraffe, but could not fit it on my

Sometimes I leave my books open on my desk
Hoping that the words from my books
will get the urge in my absence
                                                              pages

                                                    their

                                        from

                              escape

                    to

and
r   o   a   m

                                        a
                              r   d
                              o
                                   u   n
my
room
and

                         FII
                    LLLLL
              LLLLLLLLL

my
mind
with

                    n p r t o
                  I s i a i n
                  ! ! ! ! ! !

when I return

(but it doesn't always work)

Philip Waddell

During the first round of their bout the circle bided its time rolling with the try angle's sharp jabs but in the second round it changed its tactics. The circle bounced out of its corner and mounted a protracted and vicious pummelling attack that soon had the try angle cornered and flagging. By the time the referee stopped the contest the try angle had been squarely beaten.

1
An
ambitious
'try' angle got
itself into shape
for a title fight with
the world champion circle.

2
Most
unfortunately,
(for the ambitious
try angle) the champ-
ion circle was not only
a skilful one but an
especially vicious
one too.

4
In fact so squarely beaten
was the try angle by the
vicious circle that it never
ever recovered. Sad to say
it remains to this day what
it became in that unequal
contest – a wrecked angle.

STUMPED

Gerda Mayer

FORESTS ARE FELLED TO MAKE ANTHOLOGIES IN PRAISE OF FORESTS IN DEFENCE OF TREES

Howard Schrager

A tidal wave of stars strokes the night,
Quiet sleep holds the silence tight
Lapping of traffic begins
Sleep stops and darkness thins
Clear air blows away
Roll back the day
Skylarks sing
Peace sin-
King

SYLLABIC SILENCE

Bethan Brooks

LITERAL LEVITATION

Nick Toczek

the carpet!

And hover high over

chair rise,

Was strange to see her

sang like a harp. It

When she sat and

surprise
It was quite a sudden

Clare Bevan

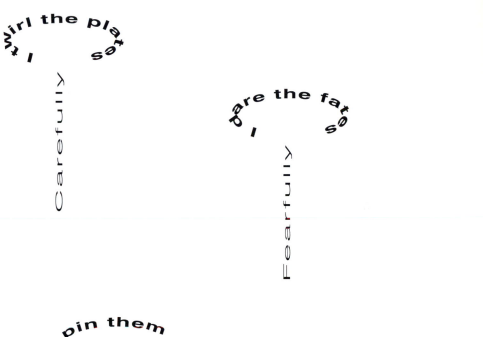

I twirl the plates
Carefully

I dare the fates
Fearfully

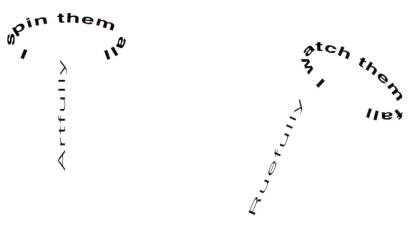

I spin them all
Artfully

I watch them fall
Ruefully

Judith Nicholls

David Wilkinson

Imagine

What

There If

Was You

Nothing Looked

And In

Me

Me

And In

Nothing Looked

Was You

There If

What

Imagone

PHARAOH NUFF

Celia Warren

Deep
inside a
pyramid, crawling
on my tummy, I came
across a sarcophagus;
inside it was a mummy. I asked,
'What's your name? Can I join you in bed?'
One answer he gave, 'Two-Kan-Kum-In,' he said.

Phillip Waddell

Ghostly footsteps in the night...

down   the
look   cinder
eyes   track –
All   the
                                       pole
                                       vault
                                       pole
                                       connects,
                                       bends
                                       back. . .
                                       the
                                       boy
                                       who's
                                       hurled
                                       above
                                       the
                                       bar
                                       returns
                                       to
                                       earth
                                       a falling
                                       star.

SKY HIGH
────────────
J. Patrick Lewis

46

I'm

sorry for   shouting.

Lets

be   pals.

I was

wrong   the   other   day.

All

those   months   of

being

friends

I've   startled   away,

Like   a   of

flock

frightened   birds.

MORE POETRY FROM WAYLAND

Wayland Poetry Collection:

Themed collections by Brian Moses, illustrated by Kelly Waldek.
27 x 22 cm, full-colour,
32 pages: £9.99 hardback and £4.99 paperback

Poems About Animals	0 7502 2437 1 hbk, 0 7502 2441 X pbk
Poems About Food	0 7502 2438 X hbk, 0 7502 2442 8 pbk
Poems About Space	0 7502 2436 3 hbk, 0 7502 2240 1 pbk
Poems About School	0 7502 2435 5 hbk, 0 7502 2439 8 pbk

Poems About Me/Poems About You and Me:

Poetry about what it means to be a member of society.
27 x 22 cm, full-colour, 32 pages, : £9.50 hbk & £4.99 paperback

ALSO AVAILABLE AS BIG BOOKS AND IN EDUCATIONAL PACKS
Big Books 44 x 36 cm, available at £13.99

Poems About You and Me	0 7502 1128 8 hbk, 0 7502 2384 7 pbk, 0 7502 2386 3 BB
Poems About Me	0 7502 1127 X hbk, 0 7502 2383 9 pbk, 07502 26781 BB

The Worst Class In School:

A5, black-and-white illustrations by Kelly Waldek. Brian Moses has collected poems
that describe the adventures of the school's — and perhaps the world's — naughtiest
class. Only one thing can save them from themselves: the arrival of Miss Honey!

The Worst Class In School   0 7502 2540 8 pbk: £3.99, 48 pages

Poems About:

Themed collections of poems for primary children.
27 x 22 cmm full-colour, £4.99 paperback only.

Poems About Families	0 7502 2397 9
Poems About Feelings	0 7502 1936 X
Poems About Journeys	0 7502 1931 9
Poems About Weather	0 7502 1930 0

TO ORDER

Contact Wayland's Customer
Services Department on:
01273 722 561,

or write to them at:
61 Western Rd, Hove,
East Sussex BN3 1JD.